Lewisham

D0345919

/ice

Library ma[...] before the last date stamped or fines will be charged at the current rate. Items can be renewed online, by telephone, letter or personal call unless required by another borrower. For hours of opening and charges see notices displayed in libraries.

Lewisham Library
199-201 Lewisham High Street
London SE13 6LG
Tel: 020 8314 9800
lewishamlibrary@lewisham.gov.uk
www.lewisham.gov.uk/libraries
24hr telephone renewals: **03333 704 700**

0 5 OCT 2017

Play

Reynolds
McCarthy

915 00000163622

a Capstone company — publishers for children

Engage Literacy is published in the UK by Raintree.
Raintree is an imprint of Capstone Global Library Limited, a company incorporated in England and Wales
having its registered office at 264 Banbury Road, Oxford, OX2 7DY – Registered company number:
6695582

www.raintree.co.uk

© 2018 by Raintree. All rights reserved. No part of this publication may be reproduced, stored in a retrieval
system, or transmitted in any way or by any means, electronic, mechanical, photocopying, recording or
otherwise, without the prior written permission of Capstone Global Library Limited.

Illustration copyright © Capstone/Mike McCarthy

Editorial credits
Clare Lewis, editor; Charmaine Whitman, designer; Steve Walker, production specialist

Image credits
Shutterstock: Kamira, 64, Pres Panayotov, 63 (bottom), Stocksnapper, 63 (top)

21 20 19 18 17
10 9 8 7 6 5 4 3 2 1
Printed and bound in China.

A Midsummer Night's Dream: A Retelling of Shakespeare's Classic Play

ISBN: 978 1 4747 4585 7

LEWISHAM LIBRARY SERVICE	
Askews & Holts	15-Aug-2017
JF	

~CONTENTS~

⟢ Introducing the Play ⟢

A Midsummer Night's Dream is a play set in ancient Athens in the country of Greece. The play takes place during a time when young women could not choose who they wanted to marry. Instead, their fathers chose for them. If a girl refused to marry her father's choice, she could be harshly punished.

Cast

Hermia   A young lady of Athens. Her father has promised her to Demetrius, but she is in love with Lysander.

Helena   A young lady of Athens. She is Hermia's oldest school friend. Helena secretly loves Demetrius.

Demetrius   A young man of Athens. He is very much in love with Hermia, and is looking forward to marrying her.

Lysander   A young man of Athens. He is in love with Hermia and agrees to run away with her.

Oberon   King of the Fairies. He is quick tempered and likes to get his own way, but he can also be kind.

Titania   Queen of the Fairies. She is kind and caring. She stands up for herself when the King disagrees with her.

Puck   A playful elf who likes to play jokes on human beings. He can make magic spells.

Bottom   A local man who is a weaver and actor. He is part of an acting troupe that is rehearsing a play to celebrate a wedding.

Snout   Another actor. He is part of the same acting troupe.

⟿ ACT 1 ⟿

Scene 1

Setting: All of Athens is excitedly preparing for the wedding of **Theseus** to **Hippolyta**. He is ruler of Athens and she is Queen of the Amazons. Two best friends, **Hermia** and **Helena**, meet in a busy street.

Hermia: Hello Helena!

Helena: Hermia!

(The friends embrace. Hermia is smiling.)

Helena: I didn't think I would see you looking so happy. I heard about your father's decision about your wedding. *(Takes a deep breath)* But I wish you and Demetrius every good fortune when you marry.

Hermia: That's not going to happen.

Helena: But surely your father has said you must marry Demetrius, or you could be punished or even harmed!

Hermia: Yes, he did say that.

Helena: So you must marry then!

Hermia: *(Shrugs)* Why? It's not fair. Athens is supposed to be a democratic society where everybody has rights. But what about women? We have the same rights as slaves do – none.

Why should my father be allowed to threaten me if I don't marry who he chooses?

Helena: But it is our way. You will bring great shame on your father unless you marry Demetrius.

Hermia:	*(Stares intently at Helena)* Helena, can I trust you?
Helena:	You know you can. We have been friends since we were little girls at school.
Hermia:	I am going to be married, but not to Demetrius. I love Lysander.
Helena:	Lysander? I suppose he is nice enough and his curly brown hair does look nice, I have to admit. But he's no Demetrius.
Hermia:	Not tall, dark and handsome, like Demetrius? But he loves me and I love him and Demetrius loves…
Helena:	*(Holding her breath)* Who?
Hermia:	*(Laughs)* Demetrius! He doesn't love me, not even a little bit. He only wants to marry me because our families arranged for us to marry when we were babies. I bet even then he looked in the mirror more than he ever looked at me.
Helena:	But Demetrius is one of the most popular young men in Athens.

Hermia: So is Lysander. I love him so much. We have a plan. I'll tell you if you are sure I can trust you.

Helena: Of course you can. Haven't we been friends forever?

Hermia: At this very moment I am due to meet Lysander by the entrance to the woods. We will run away and hide tonight and tomorrow we will find a chapel where we shall marry. I'm sure my father will accept this marriage once it has happened.

Helena: Your father will be so angry! And what about Demetrius? His heart will be broken.

Hermia: Ha! He will be angry that he isn't getting his own way, but it will be too late. Look, the sun is about to set. He will be waiting for me. Wish me luck, dear friend.

Helena: *(Gripping Hermia's hands tightly)* I wish you all the luck in this world and the next. I am glad to hear that you will not marry Demetrius.

Hermia: You have always been a good friend to me. I hope you find someone to love you as Lysander loves me. Farewell.

Exit Hermia

Helena: (*To herself*) Hermia, you are a fool. If Demetrius wanted to marry me, I would be the happiest woman in Athens. Maybe if Demetrius knew that she loved someone else, he would grow to hate her. I could comfort him and perhaps he could learn to love *me*.

Enter Demetrius

Demetrius: Helena!

Helena: (*Jumps*) Demetrius! You gave me a fright.

Demetrius: What were you thinking? You looked very serious.

Helena: Nothing... Actually, there is something. And it's about you.

Demetrius: (*Smiling*) Has the lovely Hermia been speaking to you?

Helena: No ... um ... yes.

Demetrius: Well, which is it?

Helena: *(Clenches her fists)* Yes. Hermia swore me to secrecy but you should know the truth. She is planning to deceive you. She and Lysander...

Demetrius: *Lysander!*

Helena: Yes, they're planning to run away from Athens and...

Demetrius: Where? Tell me where Hermia is!

Helena: Why do you want to know? She has left you. She loves another man. Why should you care where she is?

Demetrius: I need to know. Tell me where she is!

Helena: The woods. But why would you want to be with somebody who doesn't love you?

Exit Demetrius

Helena: Wait!

Exit Helena

Scene 2

Setting: Deep within the woods, Titania, Queen of the Fairies is arguing with her husband, Oberon, King of the Fairies. The queen wishes to look after a human boy who was the son of her friend. The king is jealous of the love she is showing the child. He wishes to care for the child himself. That way, he won't have to share Titania's love and attention.

Titania: I promised his poor dying mother that I would look after her only child myself.

Oberon: But I will bring him up to be a strong man. He is better under my care.

Titania: But I will give him a mother's love. The boy will stay under my care.

Oberon: You are my wife. You must listen to what I say.

Titania: I will listen to you, but I will do what I wish. I love him and I want to care for him myself.

Oberon: You must obey me – I am the king.

Titania: And I am the queen. I have to go and look after him now, poor child.

Exit Titania

Oberon: Once she said she only loved me. But now she argues with me and says she loves this boy. She needs to learn to do what I say. I could teach the boy about the forest. Then I wouldn't have to share Titania's love with him or anyone. Puck!

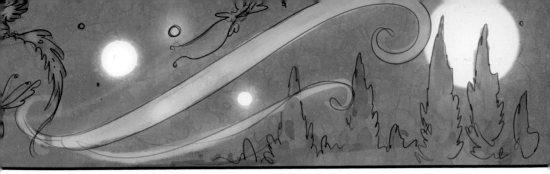

Enter Puck

Puck: King Oberon. *(Bows)* At your service.

Oberon: The queen will learn not to disobey me. Puck, fly fast and fetch the flower called "Love in Idleness". I will make a love potion from it. I'll slip it into the queen's eyes when she is asleep. If she is so full of love, then let her fall in love with the first living thing she sees. Hopefully it will be a bear, or wolf, or meddling monkey. How I will laugh to see her fall in love with a beast of the forest!

Puck: *(Laughing)* I will return soon, my king.

Exit Puck

Oberon: Titania will be sorry she argued with me.

~ACT 2~

Scene 1

Setting: Oberon is waiting in the woods. He hides when he hears voices coming nearer.

Helena: Wait, Demetrius. I have to tell you something.

Demetrius: I have no time to listen to you. I need to find Hermia before she makes a big mistake.

Helena: Please, stop.

Demetrius: *(Turning around)* Go away, Helena.

Helena: But I love you.

Demetrius: You think that will make me happy and make me forget Hermia? You're wrong! When I find Lysander, I will make him leave. Hermia will love me instead.

Helena: I have wanted to tell you how I feel for so many years.

Demetrius: You should have stayed silent. I don't want to hear it.

Helena: But I do love you.

Demetrius: I do not, nor can I ever, love you. You are nothing to me. I love Hermia.

Helena: That just makes me love you even more.

Demetrius: You will never be beautiful like Hermia in my eyes. When I look at you, I feel sick.

Helena: And I am sick when I do not look at you.

Demetrius: I will run away from you and leave you alone with the wild beasts of the woods. That is how little I care about you.

Exit Demetrius

Helena: I will follow Demetrius. I have to make him understand.

Exit Helena

Oberon: *(Comes out from behind a tree)* That poor young woman. Her heart is broken. I know what it feels like when the one you love loves somebody else. Titania once loved only me. Now she pours her love on this child she wants to care for. She has no time for me anymore. Perhaps I can help these humans to find love in the right place.

Enter Puck

Puck: Flower delivery!

Oberon: Well done, Puck. *(He breaks off a flower.)* I will use this on the queen. I also have another job for you. Go deep into the forest where you will see a young man and woman. When they fall asleep, squeeze some of the love potion from this flower into the eyes of the man. When he wakes, he will fall in love with the first thing he sees. It will be Helena, the woman who loves him.

Puck: Of course. I will do as you command.

Oberon: My good Puck. Be gone.

Exit Puck

Oberon: Now I need to find Titania. *(Walks down the forest path. Titania lies there fast asleep.)* There you are. I will squeeze the juice of this flower into your eyes. When you wake up you will fall madly in love with the first thing you see. Be it cat or bear, or a boar with bristled hair. That will teach you not to love another. Here we go. *(Squeezes the love potion into Titania's eyes)*

Exit Oberon

Scene 2

Setting: Puck finds two people asleep. He wrongly thinks it is Helena and Demetrius, but it is Hermia and Lysander.

Puck: Ahhh. Here they are. I will place the love potion in this man's eyes. He will fall in love with the first thing he sees. This lovely woman whose heart he has broken. *(Squeezes the love potion into the eyes of Lysander)*

Exit Puck

Enter Helena

Helena: *(Seeing Lysander lying on the forest floor)*
Lysander, are you dead or alive?
Has Demetrius harmed you with
his sword?

Lysander: *(Starting)* Helena. Oh gentle Helena.
Your beautiful dark hair. Your
stunning deep brown eyes. Oh, I love
you with all my heart!

Helena: *(Confused)* Hush. You are making fun
of me. You love Hermia, not me.

Lysander: Hermia is boring. I am young and
I was foolish, but now I know who
I really love. Not Hermia but *you,*
dear Helena.

Helena: The man I love has told me that he
hates me, and now you make fun
of me by pretending to love me. I
thought you were a gentleman. This is
too unkind, and I won't stay to listen
to it. Farewell.

Exit Helena

Lysander: *(To the sleeping Hermia)* Hermia, stay asleep. Never come near me again. The sight of you makes my stomach sick. Helena is my true love now. I live to honour her and to be her knight! I must find her.

Exit Lysander

Hermia: *(Waking)* Lysander, I had a terrible dream that you sat smiling as a snake ate my heart away. I know you would never be so cruel. Lysander! Where are you? I need to find you.

Exit Hermia

Scene 3

Setting: Titania is asleep. A group of men enter. They are looking for somewhere to practise the play that they are putting on to celebrate the wedding of Theseus and Hippolyta.

Bottom: Well, here we are. This is a perfect spot to rehearse our play. We need to get it ready in time for the wedding celebration for Theseus and Hippolyta.

Snout: They will reward us well if we please them, Bottom. Let's make sure we practise the play well.

Bottom: Come on then, let's get started!

Enter Puck

Puck: *(Quietly from behind a tree)* What have we here? A group of mortal men. I can have a little fun here! I shall improve the looks of the one they call Bottom. I will give him the head of a donkey. *(Waves his arms. Bottom has the head of a donkey.)*

Snout: Agghhh!

Bottom: What is wrong?

Snout: You have changed. It's terrible magic!

Bottom: What on earth do you mean? I haven't changed. I am the same person I always was. Hee haw. Hee haw. Wait, why did I say that? Hee haw.

Snout: Run away! Bottom is now a monster not a man.

Bottom: Wait! Hee haw. Hee haw. *(The men flee, screaming, leaving Bottom behind.)*

Puck: *(Coming out from behind a tree)* How easy it is to make fun of these mortals!

Enter Oberon

Oberon: *(Hiding)* I will stay behind this tree.

Titania: *(The love potion is working on her.)* What is that noise? I was asleep. Ahh – you are so beautiful!

Bottom: Who are you talking to? Is there somebody behind me? Hee haw.

Titania: I'm talking to you, of course!

Bottom: Me? Hee haw. Why do I keep saying that? Hee haw. Hee haw.

Titania: I love you from the tips of your toes to the tips of your long furry ears.

Bottom: What? I know I'm a bit hairy, but I don't think it's fair to describe me as furry. Hee haw. I've said it again! Hee haw.

Titania: Oh I love your deep voice. I love all your funny little ways.

Bottom: But how can you love me? I am a very simple man. With a simple man's face. Hee haw. And my ears... *(Touches ears)* Wait, they are the ears of a donkey! Hee haw. I am half man, half donkey! Hee haw. What has happened to me?

Titania: You are perfect. I will give you whatever you want. Silk clothes or a bale of the best hay. Just ask.

Bottom: This ... hee haw ... is very strange. But I am hungry. Hee haw!

Titania: Come with me. I love you and will look after you forever.

Exit Bottom and Titania

Oberon: Titania, you are so proud. You argue with me. Yet here you are in love with a stupid donkey. Hee haw indeed. Your love makes you look like a fool.

Exit Oberon

Scene 4

Enter Hermia and Demetrius

Hermia: Where is Lysander? What have you done to him?

Demetrius: I haven't done anything to him.

Hermia: I had a terrible dream that he hated me.

Demetrius: Perhaps it's true. Then you and I can wed!

Hermia: I don't love you, and I don't care if I never see you again. Get out of my way. I just want Lysander. Where are you, Lysander?

Exit Hermia

Demetrius: It's no use talking to Hermia when she's like this. My legs ache with tiredness from chasing her. My head will work better after a sleep.

(Demetrius curls up and falls asleep.)

Enter Oberon and Puck

Oberon: Puck, there is something wrong. This man Demetrius still loves Hermia. I just saw the fair maid, Helena, being chased by the man called Lysander. Didn't you give the love potion to this man? Helena loves Demetrius. I wanted him to love her back.

Puck: I just saw a sleeping couple and assumed it was the humans you meant. I didn't wake them up to find out their names.

Oberon: You have put the love potion into the wrong man's eyes! We must make this right. I will put love potion in the sleeping eyes of this man, Demetrius. You will find Helena and bring her here. She has dark hair and a sad, sad face.

Exit Puck

Oberon: Here, young Demetrius. I will gently squeeze this love potion into your eyes and you will fall in love with the first person you spy. I hope it will be Helena.

(Oberon kneels over Demetrius.)

Oberon: There, it's done. I hear a sound.

Enter Puck

Puck: Helena is coming.

Oberon: Great. Demetrius will hear her and wake up. When he sees her, he will fall in love with her as I planned. Come and hide behind this tree with me, and we will watch together.

Enter Lysander and Helena

Lysander:　Why do you think I'm making fun of you, Helena? Why won't you believe that I love you?

Helena:　You ran away with Hermia. It is clear that you love *her*.

Lysander:　I was just a foolish boy, but now I have grown up.

Helena:　It was only hours ago that you said you loved Hermia. And I love another – Demetrius.

Lysander:　Demetrius loves only Hermia. He does not love you.

Demetrius: *(Waking and affected by the love potion)* O Helena, goddess, perfect one. You are my love.

Helena: You are cruel to make fun of me, Demetrius, when I know you and Lysander both love Hermia.

Lysander: It is unkind, Demetrius. We know you love Hermia and I am now happy for you to marry her. But let me love Helena. I will love her until I die.

Helena: Stop this!

Demetrius: Lysander, you can keep Hermia. My love for her has gone. It is Helena who I love now.

Lysander: Helena, don't believe him. He does not love you.

Helena: Neither of you loves me. I don't know what is wrong with you both.

43

Enter Hermia

Hermia: Lysander, there you are. Why did you leave me alone in the forest?

Lysander: Stay away, Hermia. My love for you is gone.

Hermia: What lie is this?

Lysander: I love Helena and her alone.

Demetrius: *I* love Helena.

Helena: Please. No more. Why do you both tease me so?

Hermia: It must be a cruel joke that they play on you. They both love me. Isn't that true? Let me take your hand, Lysander.

Lysander: Stay away from me, Hermia, you vile thing. Helena, it is you that I love.

Demetrius: Helena, I love you more than Lysander ever could.

Hermia: What have you done, Helena, to steal the heart of Lysander? You were my friend. I shared my secret with you!

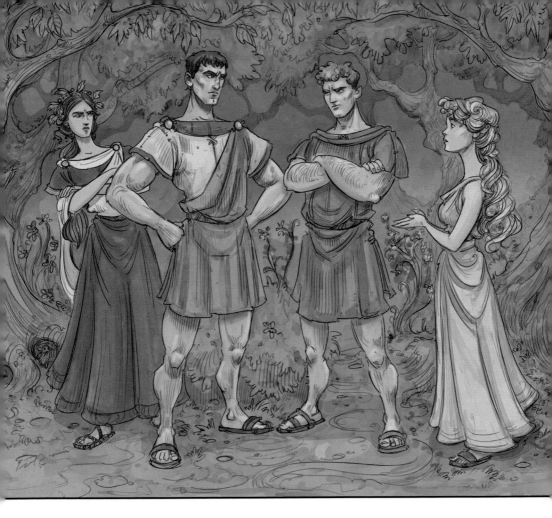

Helena: I have been your good friend for many years. I have always kept your secrets even when we were at school. This one time I did not. I told Demetrius that you had fled with Lysander into the woods. I followed him and he told me to go away. But now they both tease me by saying that they love me. Did you tell them to do this, Hermia? You're making me look like a fool.

Demetrius: My love for you is true, Helena. Let me prove it to you.

Lysander: Do not listen to him! My love for you is even truer.

Helena: I don't want to listen to these lies anymore. Let me go back to Athens.

Hermia: Well go, then. I don't want you around. You've caused nothing but trouble. Why are you even here?

Helena: Because my heart still loves one of these men.

Hermia: Who, Lysander?

Helena: Demetrius, of course.

Lysander: You say that, Helena, because you are scared of what Hermia may do to you if you admit you love me. Don't worry, I will save you from her.

Demetrius: But *I* love you the most, and *I* will protect you from Hermia.

Helena: It's true that I am scared of her. When she is angry, she is mean. She was always quarrelsome when she went to school. She is little, but fierce.

Hermia: Lysander! Demetrius! Why are you listening to Helena's lying words?

Lysander: Go away, Hermia. Nobody wants you here. I will not let you hurt Helena.

Demetrius: Neither will I.

Lysander: I will fight you, Demetrius, to see who deserves the lovely Helena.

Hermia: But what about me?

Lysander: You are nothing to me. I shudder when I see your face. Demetrius, let us settle this now.

Exit Demetrius and Lysander

Helena: I will not stay here alone with you, Hermia. I don't trust you, and I know you wish me harm. I will run fast away from you.

Exit Helena

Hermia: Has the world gone mad? My love, Lysander, says he doesn't love me. Demetrius wanted to marry me, but all he can think of is Helena. I must find Lysander again.

Exit Hermia

(Oberon and Puck appear from behind the tree where they have been watching.)

Oberon: This is all our fault. Puck, you must create a thick fog over the woods. Copy the voices of the humans so they follow you. We will put them all to sleep and make right our wrongs.

Puck: I shouldn't have given Bottom a donkey's head either. I thought it would be funny, but now I feel sorry for the queen. She wouldn't want to be in love with a donkey! And I gave the love potion to Lysander instead of Demetrius, but it was a mistake. I want to help you make everything right.

Oberon: You will, Puck. I shouldn't have given the queen the love potion. Together we will undo all that we have done wrong.

Exit Puck

Oberon: I hope it is not too late to make Titania forgive me. I miss her, and we were fools to argue. I shall remove the love spell from her and she, alone, shall choose who she wishes to love. If I have to share her love, I will.

⁓ACT 3⁓

Scene 1

Setting: A strange fog covers the woods. It is not possible to see through.

Enter Lysander and Puck

Lysander: Where are you, Demetrius? This thick fog hides you.

Puck: *(Pretending to be Demetrius)* Come here now, villain, as I am ready to fight you. Where are you hiding?

Lysander: I will join you right now.

Puck: Follow me. I know where there is a flat, clear piece of land in the middle of the forest. We will have our fight there.

Exit Lysander

Enter Demetrius

Demetrius: Lysander! Speak! Have you run away, you coward? Are you hiding?

Puck: *(Pretending to be Lysander)* Come and find me. I am waiting.

Demetrius: Yes, but where are you?

Puck: Follow my voice.

Exit Demetrius

Enter Lysander

Lysander: Demetrius is always just ahead of me. I come when he calls, but then he has gone. I have chased and chased him, but he is too fast. Now I am lost in this dark place. *(Lies down.)* I will rest here until daylight.

Enter Demetrius

Puck: *(Pretending to be Lysander)* Demetrius, you are such a scaredy cat.

Demetrius: Stay still, instead of running away. You are too scared for us to meet. Where are you now?

Puck: *(Still pretending to be Lysander)* I am here.

Demetrius: You are here. You are there. Go away. *(Lies down)* I shall rest, but will search for you when it is daylight.

Enter Helena

Helena: Oh long night. I have to wait for daylight to go back to Athens. *(Lies down)* Time will go faster if I sleep.

Puck: One, two, three asleep. But I need one more. Ah, here she comes.

Enter Hermia

Hermia: I have never felt so tired nor so sad. My legs will not work anymore. At least this fog should hide Lysander from the sword of Demetrius. *(Lies down)* I shall rest until daybreak.

Puck: Now they are all sound asleep. I will squeeze some of the love potion juice in Lysander's eyes. When he awakes he will fall in love once again with Hermia. Demetrius will still love Helena. All will be well.

Scene 2

Bottom: Those oats tasted yummy.

Titania: There will be more for you after we sleep. I cannot keep my eyes open. Oh, how I love you. *(Falls asleep)*

Bottom: Hee haw. *(Drifts off to sleep)*

Enter Puck and Oberon

Oberon: I was angry with the queen, which was wrong. I should have talked with her instead of planning a trick. Puck, take off the donkey's head from this poor man. When he awakes, he will think it was all a dream. But first I will release Titania from my spell. *(Oberon waves his arms over Titania.)*

Titania: *(Waking and unable to remember that she has been in love with Bottom)* My Oberon! I have had the strangest dream. I thought I was in love with a donkey.

Oberon: Look. There lies your love.

Titania: What do you mean? Are you joking? I would never love a donkey.

Oberon: Puck, remove the donkey's head. Come, Titania, take my hand. Let us not quarrel anymore. I don't care if you want to share your love between me and the child. Let's care for him together.

Puck: It's nearly morning. The sun is rising in the east.

Oberon: We must fly away and hide. The day does not belong to us. We are creatures of the night.

Titania: While we are flying, you can tell me what happened and why I woke up sleeping with these mortals on the ground.

Oberon: It is a long story, my love.

Titania: We will make our journey just long enough so that you can tell me, my sweet. And then we will not quarrel anymore.

Exit Oberon and Titania

Bottom:	*(Waking up and feeling his head)* My head, my head. Is it covered in fur? It feels normal. Why did I think that I had the head of a donkey? It must have just been a dream, and yet it felt so real. I must hurry and find my friends so we can put on the play at the wedding!

Exit Bottom (loudly)

Hermia:	What is that noise I hear? What are we all doing here?
Lysander:	Are you sure we are awake? My dreams have been full of the strangest things.
Hermia:	I dreamt that you no longer loved me.
Lysander:	It must have been a dream. A nightmare. I love you, of course.
Helena:	I dreamed that you, Demetrius, loved me.
Demetrius:	That was no dream. I do love you, sweet Helena.
Helena:	He sounds as if he is telling you the truth.
Hermia:	He is telling you the truth. Look at him! You should be happy!

Lysander: Let us all return to Athens. On the way we can tell each other our dreams.

Hermia: And I'm sure they *are* all dreams. We must remember that.

Exit Hermia, Lysander, Helena and Demetrius

Puck: *(Speaking to the audience)* All returned to Athens where Lysander and Hermia were married, as were Helena and Demetrius. Snout, Bottom and the other actors performed their play. Oberon and Titania congratulated them on their marriages, and they all lived long, happy lives.

I hope you all enjoyed this play, but if you didn't, pretend it was but a dream – a midsummer night's dream. Good night to you all.

Shakespeare's Midsummer Night's Dream

The playwright, William Shakespeare, was born in 1564 in Stratford-upon-Avon. He wrote and co-wrote more than 40 plays in his life.

Shakespeare's play, *A Midsummer Night's Dream* was first performed in 1595 or 1596. It would have been performed during daylight on a simple stage without any backdrops. All the female roles were taken by male actors.

William Shakespeare

Shakespeare's Globe Theatre in London, shows how theatres would have looked in Shakespeare's time.

In Shakespeare's time, most of the audience watching *A Midsummer Night's Dream* would have stood up in the "groundings". It only cost a penny, but they would have to be ready to stand up for two to three hours. For an extra penny, you could buy a seat on the bench around the yard. Another penny would give you the comfort of having a cushion to sit on.

Inside Shakespeare's Globe Theatre, you can stand where some of the audience would have stood near the stage to view the play.

Since then, the play has been performed thousands of times, all over the world. Perhaps you could put on your own production!